THEORY IS
GRADE 1

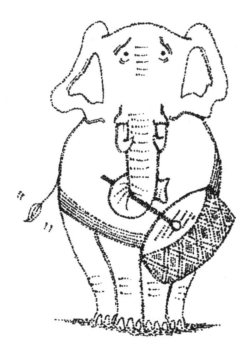

Maureen Cox

First published 1988
by **Subject Publications**

Revised 1990
New edition 1993
Sixteenth impression 2013

ISBN 0 9516940 8 1

Cover illustrated by Emma Nicholson

Printed by Pardy & Son (Printers) Ltd.,
Parkside, Ringwood, Hampshire, BH24 3SF

Tel: +44 (0)1425 471433
Fax: +44 (0)1425 478923
Email: sales@pardy.co.uk

For Flora

★ ★ ★ ★ ★ ★

If you want to play an instrument properly, sing well or just improve your listening, you need to read music and understand theory.

This book takes you through the theory of music in a simple, straightforward way. There are plenty of fun pictures and things to do. You will find a variety of interesting puzzles and questions to test yourself. At the end of the book there is a dictionary of musical terms, a list of signs and a progress chart for you to use.

With my help you can take your first step on the road to mastering and enjoying the theory of music. With this book you can discover that Theory is Fun.

MJC

Acknowledgements

I am grateful to the many Professional Private Music Teachers and Members of the Incorporated Society of Musicians who use *Theory is Fun* with their pupils and I should especially like to thank Alison Bowditch, Christina Bourne, Brenda Harris, Alison Hogg, Judith Homes, Ann Leggett and Marion Martin for their very constructive comments and helpful suggestions.

Maureen Cox

CONTENTS

THE TREBLE CLEF

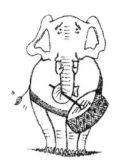

This is a treble clef.

Can you finish these treble clefs?

Draw a treble clef in each space.

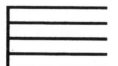

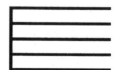

LETTER NAMES

The notes **E G B D F** sit on the lines.

E   G   B   D   F

Elephant **G**eorge **B**eats **D**rum **F**ast

The notes **F A C E** sit in the spaces.

F   A   C   E

 Think of the happy face and you will remember the notes . . . . . **F A C E**

Name the notes

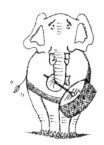

Show Elephant George how well you know the notes in the treble clef.

Remember the happy face.

Name the notes...

____

____

____

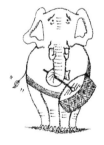

Count how many
you had right.

Put the number
in the box.

The lost puppy

Fill in the names of the notes.

Tom looked into the water.
He saw his

_ _ _ _ looking back at him.

Suddenly he saw another
_ _ _ _

next to his.

It was a puppy.

It looked lost.

"I wonder what
_ _ _ it is?"
thought Tom.

The lost puppy...

The puppy looked hungry.

Tom had a biscuit in his pocket.

Should he  it?

Then Tom saw a boy.   He was calling,

"   !"

 Tom was happy.   The puppy

was not lost any more.

When you are ready to test yourself on the treble clef letter names, turn over to page 12.

Write the words

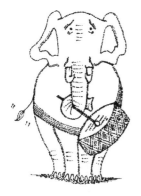

How many did
you get right?

Put the number
in the box.

Write the notes

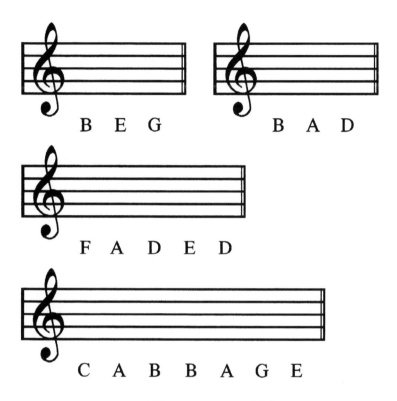

B E G   B A D

F A D E D

C A B B A G E

How many did
you get right?

Put the number
in the box. ↘

18

THE BASS CLEF

This is a bass clef.

Draw a bass clef in each space.

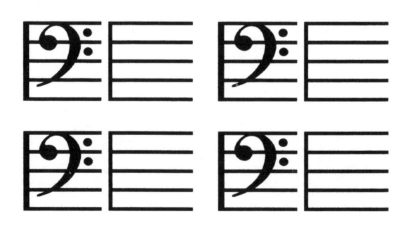

LETTER NAMES

The notes **G B D F A** sit on the lines.

G   B   D   F   A

Georgina Bear Deserves Food Always

The notes **A C E G** sit in the spaces.

A   C   E   G

All Cats Enjoy Grieg

Name the notes

Show Georgina Bear how well you know the notes in the bass clef.

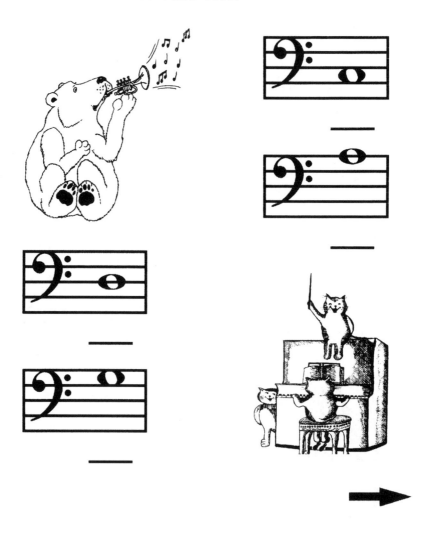

Name the notes...

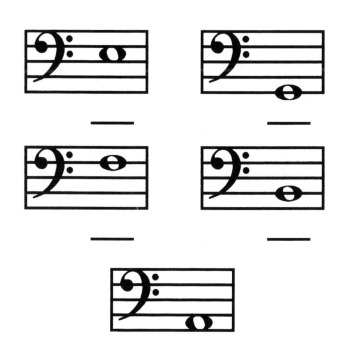

___   ___

___   ___

___

Put a number in the
box to show how
many you had right.

Life on the farm

Fill in the names of the notes.

 Early one morning the farmer

took a _ _ _ of corn and

set out to _ _ _ _

the chickens.

They were pleased to see him. First of all

the farmer took an _ _ _

from his best hen.

Life on the farm...

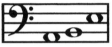

He showed it to his son — — — who
was in the cowshed milking the cows.

"What a fine — — — ,"

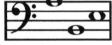

said — — — . Then the farmer went
to the field and looked at

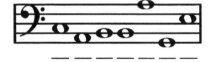

a — — — — — — — —

to see if it was ready to cut for dinner.

When you are ready to test yourself on the
bass clef letter names, turn over to page 20.

Write the words

— — —

— — — —

— — —

— — — —

 How many did
you get right?

Put the number
in the box. ↘

Write the notes

A   D   D   C   A   F   E

B   E   G   G   E   D

B   A   G   G   A   G   E

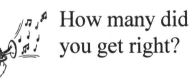 How many did
you get right?

Put the number
in the box. → 20

More notes

You know all the notes which are on the lines and in the spaces. There are other notes which sit on top and underneath - like this...

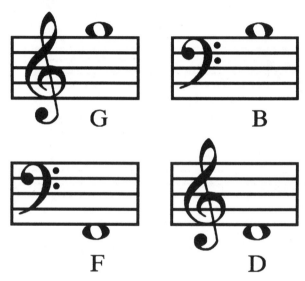

Both these two notes are **middle C.**

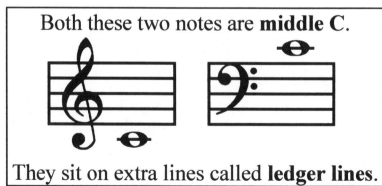

They sit on extra lines called **ledger lines**.

Test yourself

Put a treble clef **or** a bass clef in front of each note to make it say its **correct name**.

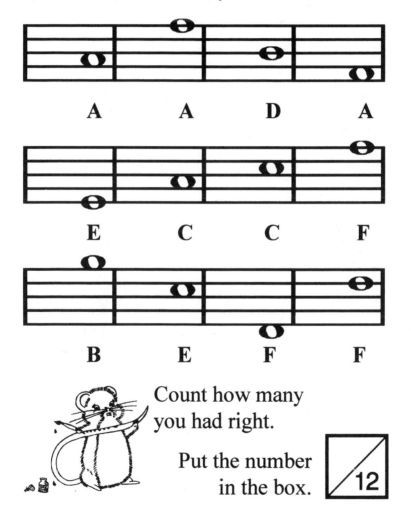

Count how many you had right.

Put the number in the box.

/12

TIME NAMES

You now know all the notes you need for Grade 1 and you know where they are on

the **stave** ➔ ≡≡≡≡≡

So far you have met only the **letter** names of notes. Notes also have **time** names.

You have met **O** the SEMIBREVE or **whole note**.

This note ♩ is a MINIM or **half note**.

2 ♩ minims ♩ = 1 semibreve

♩ + ♩ = **O**

Both time names are used in Grade 1.

NOTE VALUES

This note ♩ is a CROTCHET or **quarter note**.

2 │crotchets♩ = 1 │minim
♩ + ♩ = 𝅗𝅥

 This note ♪ is a QUAVER or **eighth note**.

2 │quavers = 1 │crotchet
♪ + ♪ = ♩

This note ♬ is a SEMIQUAVER or **sixteenth note**.

2 │semiquavers = 1 ♪quaver
♬ + ♬ = ♪

Notice how notes worth less than a crotchet can be joined together or **beamed**.

The Note Pyramid

The note pyramid is very useful.
You can see at a glance the values
of notes.

 For example, you can see that a
semibreve is worth two minims or
sixteen semiquavers!

Test Your Observation

 Use the **note pyramid** to put the correct number in each space.

A **semibreve** = ☐ minims,

☐ crotchets,

☐ quavers,

☐ semiquavers.

A **minim** = ☐ crotchets,

☐ quavers,

☐ semiquavers.

A **crotchet** = ☐ quavers,

☐ semiquavers.

There are ☐ crotchets in a semibreve

☐/10

Wordsearch

T	R	H	A	R	P	M	Q	U	V
R	E	V	A	U	Q	I	M	E	S
M	L	A	D	N	U	N	R	V	L
E	I	M	I	T	A	I	N	E	S
O	P	N	B	H	V	M	R	R	T
H	U	R	I	A	E	L	C	B	A
J	Y	W	B	M	R	T	N	I	P
G	R	E	T	S	C	R	O	M	E
M	I	C	R	O	T	C	H	E	T
R	E	A	S	R	O	Q	U	S	X

Find the **time names**

1. _____

2. _____

3. _____

4. _____

5. _____

Where shall I put the stem?

The stems of notes are on the left when they go down.

 The stems are on the right when they go up.

If a note is written above the middle line, its stem goes down.

 When a note is written below the middle line, its stem goes up.

If a note is written on the middle line,  its stem can go up or down.

DOTTED NOTES

A dot after a note is worth **half** the value of the note.

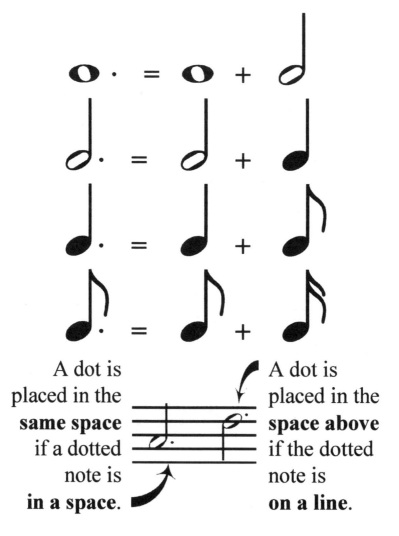

A dot is placed in the **same space** if a dotted note is **in a space.**

A dot is placed in the **space above** if the dotted note is **on a line**.

Test yourself

Fill in the missing numbers.

1. ♪ = ☐ semiquavers

2. 𝅝 = ☐ crotchets

3. ♩ = ☐ quavers

4. 𝅝. = ☐ minims

5. ♩. = ☐ quavers

6. ♩. = ☐ crotchets

7. ♩. = ☐ quavers

8. 𝅝. = ☐ quavers

Write one note

for your

answer ↘

9. ♩. ♪ =

10. ♩ ♩ ♩ =

How many did you have right? ➡ ☐/10

page 31

Do you know all your notes?

Draw:-

(1) a **semibreve** in each **space** of the stave.

(2) a **crotchet** on each **line** of the stave.

(3) a **minim** in each **space** of the stave.

(4) a **quaver** on each **line** of the stave.
The 'tail' is on the right-hand side of the stem.

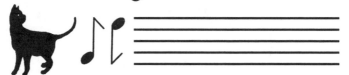

(5) a minim on middle C.

Draw:-

(6) a **semiquaver** in each **space** of the stave. Remember - right-hand side for tails.

(7) **two quavers** joined together in the **C space.**

(8) **two semiquavers** joined together on the **G line.**

(9) a **dotted minim** in each **space**.

(10) a **dotted crotchet** on each **line**.

TIED NOTES

A tie joins notes which are
at the same pitch
[the notes sound the same]
play   *hold*

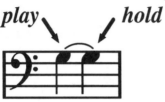

Tied notes are joined together at the **heads** (not the stems) and from the **outside** (not the inside) of each head.

You can join more than two notes with ties as long as they are the **same notes** and are **next to each other**. ↘

Count the beats

How many crotchet beats is each tie worth?

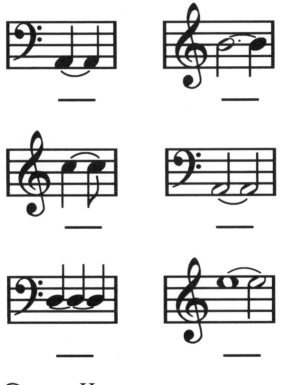

 How many answers did you have right? → ☐ 6

RESTS

There are times in music when we need to be absolutely quiet.   In order to do this, we use **rests** instead of notes.

Semibreve   Minim   Crotchet

Quaver   Semiquaver

If you want to rest for the length of a **dotted** note, put a **dot** after the rest.

Now put the correct **rest** to match each note:-

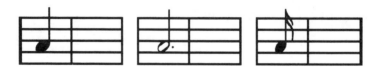

There are two ways to write a **crotchet** rest. The one you have met so far is the easiest, but the one below is very impressive if you can copy it accurately.

It looks like a **c** with a **z** on top.

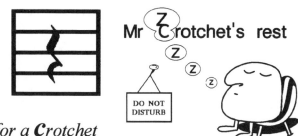

snooZe for a Crotchet

Try to match the rests with the notes **without** looking back at the last page:-

How many were correct? ♪

I expect you have noticed in your music that there are sometimes signs in front of notes. These signs are called **accidentals**. There are three accidentals - the sharp, the flat and the natural.

1. The Sharp

It looks like this ➡

It is written **in front** of a note and makes that note one semitone **higher**.

Write a sharp ♯ **in front** of each crotchet.

Accidentals...

2. The Flat

It looks like a small letter b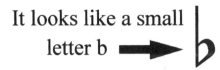

It is written **in front** of a note and makes that note one semitone **lower**.

Write a flat ♭ **in front** of each minim.

Write the following:-
1. E♭ on a line
2. A♭ in a space
3. G♯ above the stave
4. D♯ below the stave

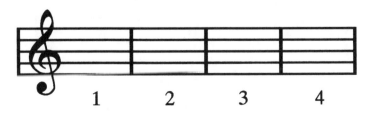

Accidentals...

3. The Natural

It looks like this ➤ It is written **in front** of a note that has been raised or lowered and it changes the note back to its normal pitch.

 This means that a natural can make a note **higher** or **lower**.

If you have an accidental in a bar of music, it changes all other notes in the bar which are at the same pitch. Take care if a note is an octave higher or lower - you will need another accidental if you want to raise or lower it.

Remember:-
Accidentals are written **in front** of notes.

The easiest way to learn about tones and semitones is to study closely a piano keyboard.

First of all, learn the names of the **white** keys. There are only seven: **ABCDEFG**

Then look at the **black** keys: they come *between* the white keys.

When you move **up the keyboard** the black keys are called **sharps**.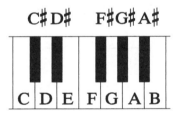

When you move **down the keyboard** the black keys are called **flats**.

Tones and Semitones...

B & C and E & F
have no black key
between them. This
means that there is
a **semitone** between B & C and E & F.

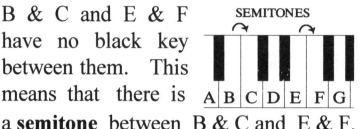

 Every step you take between
a **black** key and a **white** key
is a **semitone**.

You take **two** steps for a **tone**.
Black keys can be sharps or flats.

Fill in the missing letter names:
D raised one semitone = __
B lowered one semitone = __
C raised one tone = __
F lowered one tone = __

KEY SIGNATURES

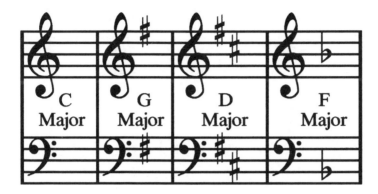

There are only
4 key-signatures for Grade 1.

C Major - has no sharps and no flats

G Major - has one sharp - F♯.

D Major - has two sharps - F♯ and C♯.

**Think of Father Christmas
and you will always
remember the order.**

F Major - has one flat - B♭.

Notice where the accidentals are written on the stave. They are **always** on these lines and spaces when they are written as key-signatures

SCALES

Now that you have met all the key-signatures for Grade 1 you are ready to learn about the scales.

1. C Major

There are no accidentals in C Major which makes it *very easy*.

Here is the scale of C Major in semibreves, **ascending** - going up.

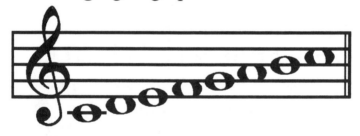

Here is the scale of C Major in semibreves, **descending** - going down.

Scales...

In **all** Major Scales there is a **semitone** between notes 3-4 and 7-8.
This ⌐¬ is how you can mark semitones.

Mark the semitones
in this scale of F Major.

Important

When descending, you find the semitones
by counting from the bottom of the scale.

2. G Major

Write the F sharps in the correct places

 in the
treble
and bass
clefs.

This is the scale of <u>G Major</u> <u>ascending</u>, <u>without</u> key-signature, in <u>crotchets</u>, in the <u>treble</u> <u>clef</u>.   Mark the <u>semitones</u>. ☹

☺ I did this for you and I underlined all the important words.   When you read a question, it is a good idea to underline all the important instructions first.

Write the scale of G Major ascending, in crotchets, with key-signature, in the bass clef. Mark the semitones.

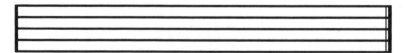

3. D Major

Write the key-signatures in the correct places in the treble and bass clefs.

Clue:-
Father
Christmas.

Write the scale of <u>D Major</u> <u>descending</u>, in <u>crotchets</u>, <u>with</u> key-signature, in the <u>treble</u> <u>clef</u>. Mark the <u>semitones</u> like this ⌐¬. ☹

☺ I did this question for you as well.

Write the scale of D Major ascending, in crotchets, without key-signature, in the treble clef. Draw ⌐¬ over each semitone.

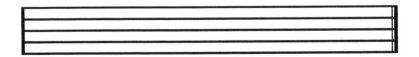

4. F Major

Write the B flats in the correct places

in the
treble
and bass
clefs.

This is the scale of F Major ascending, without key-signature, in minims, in the bass clef.　　The semitones are shown like this: ⌐¬.

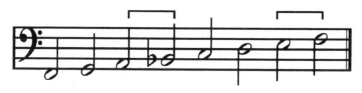

Write the scale of F Major descending, in minims, with key-signature, in the treble clef.　　Mark the semitones.　　[Underline the important words before you write.]

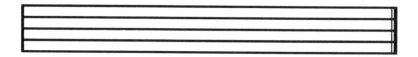

Degrees of the Scale

The first note of the scale is called the key-note or the *first degree*. Therefore the second note is the *2nd degree*, the third, the *3rd degree* and so on, until you reach the *8th degree* or *octave* - written as *8ve*.

Write the degree of the scale which is asked for. I have written the first answer for you. ☺

F Major

3rd   1st   8ve   4th

D Major

2nd   5th   7th   6th

How many did you get right?

/8

INTERVALS

An interval is the difference in pitch between two notes.

For example, in D Major there is an interval of a 3rd between D and F.

I have written the scale of D Major to show you each interval.

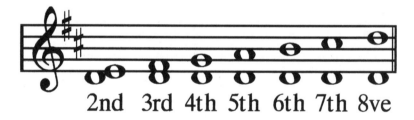

2nd   3rd   4th   5th   6th   7th   8ve

Write the intervals for G Major in the same way.

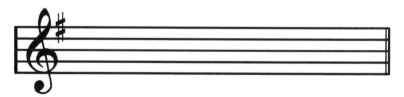

The Melodic Interval

 This is a **Melodic Interval**. The two notes are written *one after the other* and are **played separately**.

Put a number below the stave to show which melodic interval has been written. I have answered the first one for you. ☺

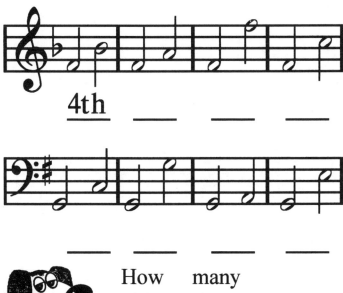

4th ___ ___ ___

___ ___ ___

How many did you have right?

The Harmonic Interval

 This interval is called a **Harmonic Interval**. The two notes are written *one above the other* and are **played at the same time**.

Write a note above each of the key-notes to make the harmonic interval. I have written the first one for you. ☺

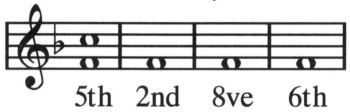

5th   2nd   8ve   6th

3rd   4th   7th   5th

SPECIAL NOTE

In Grade 1 you just call each interval 2nd, 3rd, 4th etc., always counting from the key-note.

TONIC TRIADS

The first note of a scale is called the key-note or the **tonic**. A tonic triad is made up of *three* notes:-

1. The key-note or tonic.

2. The 3rd degree (note) of the scale.

3. The 5th degree (note) of the scale.

Sometimes you will be asked to write a tonic triad **with** key-signature, sometimes *without* key-signature. At Grade 1 level this will only be a problem in D Major where the 3rd note is F#.

Tonic Triads...

Write
tonic triads
with
key-signature

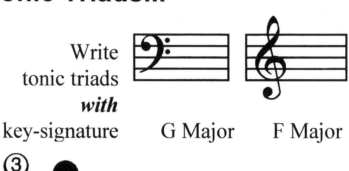

G Major   F Major

Check
these
first

☐/4

Write
tonic triads
without
key-signature

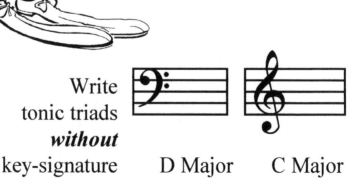

D Major   C Major

Test Yourself

Write these tonic triads:
with key-signature in the ***treble clef***.

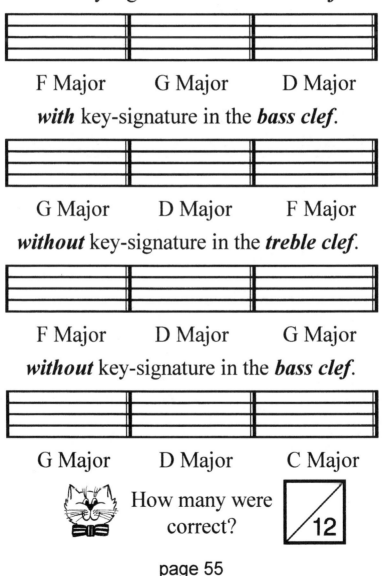

F Major   G Major   D Major

with key-signature in the ***bass clef***.

G Major   D Major   F Major

without key-signature in the ***treble clef***.

F Major   D Major   G Major

without key-signature in the ***bass clef***.

G Major   D Major   C Major

How many were correct? ⟋ 12

TIME SIGNATURES

At the beginning of a piece of music you will find a clef, a key-signature (*not* C Major) and *two numbers* which we call a **time signature**.

The order is always the same and you can remember it because the words are in alphabetical order:-

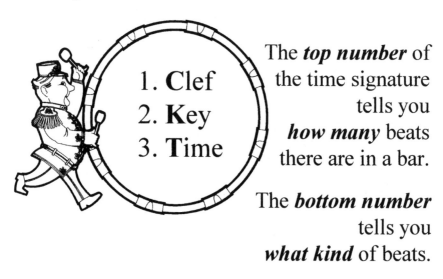

1. **Clef**
2. **Key**
3. **Time**

The *top number* of the time signature tells you *how many* beats there are in a bar.

The *bottom number* tells you *what kind* of beats.

Simple Duple Time

In Grade 1 you will only meet one simple **duple** time signature. [duple means two]

That time is $\frac{2}{4}$ time.

The top number [**2**] tells us that there are two beats in a bar.

The bottom number [**4**] tells us they are crotchets or quarter notes.

Here is a passage of music in $\frac{2}{4}$ time.

I have left out **two bar-lines**. Can you put them in for me?

Notice the *double bar-line* which comes at the end of a piece of music. It is written as a *thin line* followed by a *thicker line*.

Simple Triple Time

The only simple **triple** time signature for Grade 1 [triple means three] is $\frac{3}{4}$ time.

Can you work out what this time signature means? Write your answer here: ↓

If you worked it out correctly, you will have written that it means 3 crotchet beats in a bar.

Simple Quadruple Time

There is only one simple **quadruple** [four] time signature for Grade 1: $\frac{4}{4}$ time.

Write down what it means here: ↓

$\frac{4}{4}$ is sometimes written as **C**.

Test yourself on time signatures

Add **one note** to each bar (under the ✻)
so that the time signature is correct.

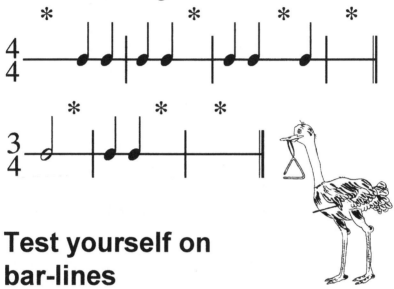

Test yourself on bar-lines

Add the missing bar-lines.

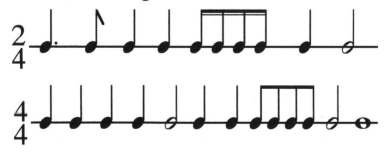

WRITING YOUR OWN MUSIC

2/4 time. If there are semiquavers, beam them together in crotchet beats. Do this with any group that has a semiquaver. ↓ ↓

3/4 time. You can beam together a whole bar of quavers. ↓

4/4 time. You can join beats 1 & 2 or 3 & 4. You *cannot* join beats 2 & 3.

SPECIAL NOTE
A **semibreve rest** ✱ is used for a whole bar's rest with all Grade 1 time signatures.

You know all the notes and rests. You have seen examples of music in Simple Time. You know all the rules. Well, now it's **your** turn!

Write a piece of music in each of the times stated:-

1. Simple Duple Time

2. Simple Triple Time

3. Simple Quadruple Time

You will be given a two-bar rhythm with a time signature and asked to write another two bars.

Hints

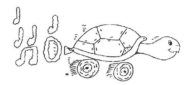

1. Take care to follow the rules for the time in which you are writing.

2. Tap the rhythm to yourself and feel how it should continue and how it should end. It would not feel right to end on a very short note such as a semiquaver.

3. You may want to use one of the rhythms given in bars one or two. That is fine as long as you put some rhythms of your own to show that you understand how to write music.

Here is a two-bar rhythm:

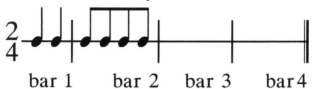

bar 1   bar 2   bar 3   bar 4

There is not *one* correct answer but *many*.
Bars 1 & 3 could have the same rhythm:

or bars 2 & 3 could have the same rhythm:

Write two-bar answering rhythms for the
following:

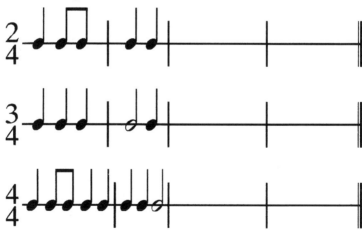

GENERAL QUESTIONS

In this exercise you will be asked *general questions* about a given passage of music.

They could be on any topic. If you have studied and understood every section in this book, you will be able to answer these questions.

Don't forget to use the dictionary and list at the end of this book to learn the musical terms and signs - they are always included.

You often have to copy some bars of a given passage. Do this very neatly.

Copy out the first two bars. Remember to put in the clef and time signature.

A DICTIONARY OF MUSICAL TERMS

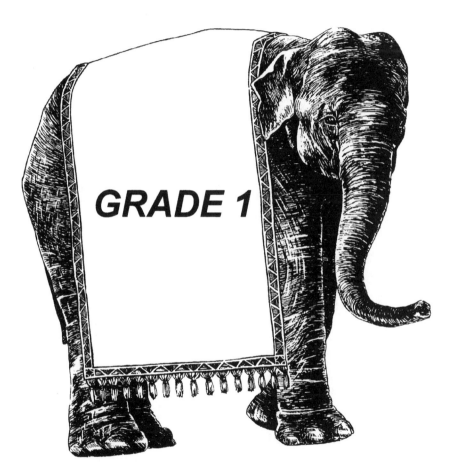

GRADE 1

AND A LIST OF SIGNS

A tempo - resume the normal speed
Accelerando - becoming gradually faster
Adagio - slow, leisurely
Allegro - lively, reasonably fast
Allegretto - slightly slower than allegro
Andante - at a walking pace
Andantino - a little slower or a little
     faster than andante
Cantabile - in a singing style
Con - with
Crescendo [cresc.] - gradually louder
Da capo [D.C.] - from the beginning
Dal segno [D.S.] - repeat from the sign 𝄋
Decrescendo [decresc.] - gradually softer
Diminuendo [dim.] - gradually softer
Dolce - sweetly
Fine - the end
Forte [f] - loud
Fortissimo [ff] - very loud
Forzando [fz] - with a strong accent
Largo - slow & stately, broad
Legato - smoothly
Leggiero - lightly
Lento - slowly

Maestoso - majestically

Mezzo forte [mf] - moderately loud

Mezzo piano [mp] - moderately soft

Moderato - at a moderate pace

Pesante - heavily

Piano [p] - soft

Pianissimo [pp] - very soft

Poco - a little

Presto - very quick

Prestissimo - as fast as possible

Rallentando [rall.] - becoming gradually
   slower

Ritardando [ritard. rit.] - gradually
   slower

Ritenuto [riten. rit.] - hold back, slower
   at once

Scherzo - a joke

Scherzando - playfully

Sforzando [sf, sfz] - with a sudden accent

Staccato - short, detached

Subito - suddenly

Tempo - speed, time

Tranquillo - quietly

Vivace - lively, quick

Music has its own language and very often signs are used instead of words.

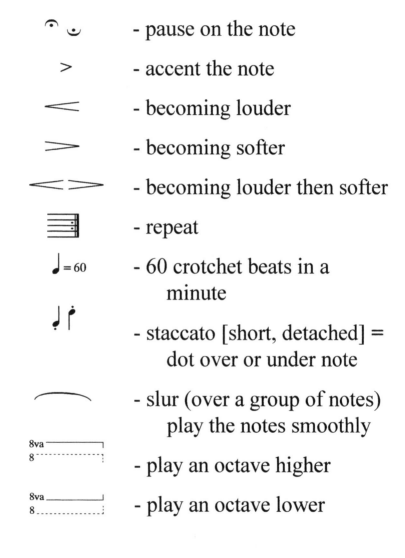

⌢ ⌣   - pause on the note

>   - accent the note

<   - becoming louder

>   - becoming softer

<>   - becoming louder then softer

▤   - repeat

♩ = 60   - 60 crotchet beats in a minute

♩ ♩   - staccato [short, detached] = dot over or under note

⌒   - slur (over a group of notes) play the notes smoothly

8va   8   - play an octave higher

8va   8   - play an octave lower

Musical terms wordsearch

E	B	A	N	D	A	N	T	E	D
O	L	O	D	E	N	I	F	E	O
A	E	L	P	A	N	V	E	L	T
O	G	C	K	L	G	V	C	O	A
C	A	N	T	A	B	I	L	E	C
P	T	M	A	R	L	V	O	X	C
T	O	B	H	G	I	A	D	O	A
P	I	A	N	O	U	C	E	T	T
N	A	S	O	I	J	E	M	I	S
D	R	A	X	E	O	Q	U	S	S

CLUES

1. At a walking pace
2. Slow, stately, broad
3. Soft
4. The end
5. Smoothly
6. In a singing style
7. Slow, leisurely
8. Lively, quick
9. Sweetly
10. Short, detached

THE NEXT STEP?

THEORY IS FUN

GRADE 2

Maureen Cox

THEORY IS FUN
GRADE 2

major and minor key signatures and scales
degrees of the scale and intervals
tonic triads
piano keyboard, tones and semitones
time signatures
grouping notes and rests, triplets
two ledger lines below and above the staves
writing four-bar rhythms
more musical terms and signs

ISBN 0 9516940 1 4

Where are **you** going?

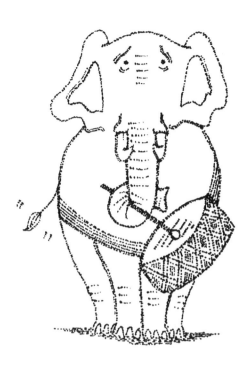

To get my
**THEORY IS FUN
GRADE 2**

PROGRESS CHART

NAME:

- Treble Clef & Letter Names ○
- Bass Clef & Letter Names ○
- Time Names & Note Values ○○
- Dotted Notes ○
- Tied Notes ○
- Rests ○
- Accidentals ○
- Tones & Semitones ○
- Key Signatures ○
- Scales & Degrees of the Scale ○
- Intervals ○
- Tonic Triads ○
- Time Signatures & Bar-lines ○
- Writing Your Own Music ○
- Answering Rhythms ○
- General Questions ○
- Dictionary of Musical Terms ○
- List of Signs ○